我们的校报

【美】艾瑞斯·哈德逊◎著
【美】布朗琪·希姆斯◎绘
范晓星◎译

天津出版传媒集团

新蕾出版社

图书在版编目（CIP）数据

我们的校报/(美)哈德逊(Hudson,I.)著；(美)
希姆斯(Sims,B.)绘；范晓星译.—天津：新蕾出版
社,2015.6(2024.12重印)
(数学帮帮忙·互动版)
书名原文：Ask Mia
ISBN 978-7-5307-6229-5

Ⅰ.①我…　Ⅱ.①哈…②希…③范…　Ⅲ.①数学–
儿童读物　Ⅳ.①O1–49
中国版本图书馆 CIP 数据核字(2015)第 096855 号
Ask Mia by Iris Hudson;
Illustrated by Blanche Sims.
Text copyright ⓒ 2006 by Iris Hudson.
Illustrations copyright ⓒ 2006 by Blanche Sims.
All rights reserved, including the right of reproduction in whole or in part in any
form. This edition published by arrangement with Kane Press, Inc. New York, NY,
represented by Lerner Publishing Group through TheChoiceMaker Korea Co.
agency.
Simplified Chinese translation copyright ⓒ 2015 by New Buds Publishing House
(Tianjin) Limited Company
ALL RIGHTS RESERVED
本书中文简体版专有出版权经由中华版权代理中心授予新蕾出版社(天津)有
限公司。未经许可,不得以任何方式复制或抄袭本书的任何部分。
津图登字：02-2012-217

出版发行：天津出版传媒集团
　　　　　新蕾出版社
http://www.newbuds.com.cn
地　　址:天津市和平区西康路 35 号(300051)
出 版 人:马玉秀
电　　话:总编办 (022)23332422
　　　　　发行部 (022)23332679　23332351
传　　真:(022)23332422
经　　销:全国新华书店
印　　刷:天津新华印务有限公司
开　　本:787mm×1092mm　1/16
印　　张:3
版　　次:2015 年 6 月第 1 版　2024 年 12 月第 22 次印刷
定　　价:12.00 元

无处不在的数学

资深编辑 卢 江

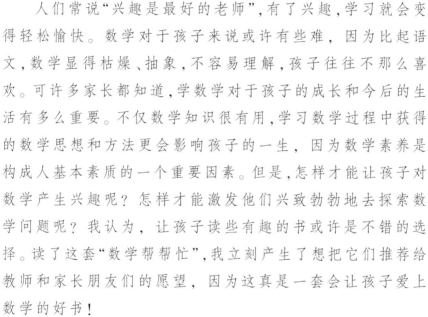

人们常说"兴趣是最好的老师",有了兴趣,学习就会变得轻松愉快。数学对于孩子来说或许有些难,因为比起语文,数学显得枯燥、抽象,不容易理解,孩子往往不那么喜欢。可许多家长都知道,学数学对于孩子的成长和今后的生活有多么重要。不仅数学知识很有用,学习数学过程中获得的数学思想和方法更会影响孩子的一生,因为数学素养是构成人基本素质的一个重要因素。但是,怎样才能让孩子对数学产生兴趣呢?怎样才能激发他们兴致勃勃地去探索数学问题呢?我认为,让孩子读些有趣的书或许是不错的选择。读了这套"数学帮帮忙",我立刻产生了想把它们推荐给教师和家长朋友们的愿望,因为这真是一套会让孩子爱上数学的好书!

这套有趣的图书从美国引进,原出版者是美国资深教育专家。每本书讲述一个孩子们生活中的故事,由故事中出现的问题自然地引入一个数学知识,然后通过运用数学知识解决问题。比如,从帮助外婆整理散落的纽扣引出分类,从为小狗记录藏骨头的地点引出空间方位等等。故事素材全部来源于孩子们的真实生活，不是童话，不是幻想，而是鲜活的生活实例。正是这些发生在孩子身边的故事，让孩子们懂得，数学无处不在并且非常有用；这些鲜活的实例也使得抽象的概念更易于理解，更容易激发孩子学习数学的兴趣，让他们逐渐爱上数学。这样的教育思想和方法与我国近年来提倡的数学教育理念是十分吻合的！

这是一套适合5~8岁孩子阅读的书，书中的有趣情节和生动的插画可以将抽象的数学问题直观化、形象化，为孩子的思维活动提供具体形象的支持。如果亲子共读的话，家长可以带领孩子推测情节的发展，探讨解决难题的办法，让孩子在愉悦的氛围中学到知识和方法。

值得教师和家长朋友们注意的是，在每本书的后面，出版者还加入了"互动课堂"及"互动练习"，一方面通过一些精心设计的活动让孩子巩固新学到的数学知识，进一步体会知识的含义和实际应用；另一方面帮助家长指导孩子阅读，体会故事中数学之外的道理，逐步提升孩子的阅读理解能力。

我相信孩子读过这套书后一定会明白，原来，数学不是烦恼，不是包袱，数学真能帮大忙！

"我想去见埃比老师，问问他校报的事。"米娅说，"你去吗？"

"当然！"我答道。

"可是艾米，"米娅说，"到时候由我来跟他讲话哟！"

米娅喜欢什么事都按照自己的方式去做。

而且大多数情况下，她都能搞定。

米娅对埃比老师说了很多很多："校报能帮助我们学习数学、科学和阅读。求您了！让我们办吧。求求您了！"

　　埃比老师笑了，他说："好吧，好吧，我同意！"

　　"谢谢您！埃比老师！"米娅说着，冲我挤了下眼睛。

　　米娅还真有办法！

需要建议吗？
来找米娅吧！

"艾米，你想做我们校报的摄影记者吗？"米娅把她的数码相机递给我，"你可以用这个。"

"好啊！"我说，"我也能写文章吗？"

"那你来参加编辑例会吧。"米娅说，"我们再商量。"

"再商量"意思就是不行呗。可那又怎么样，用米娅的相机拍拍照也一定很好玩儿。

艾拉、路易斯和乔伊也来参加编辑例会了。

"我们校报的主题是什么？"艾拉问。

"笑话！"路易斯说，"同学们可以投稿。"

"这不太好。"米娅说，"我已经请同学们把稿件投给知心姐姐栏目了。"

"知心姐姐？"艾拉问。

"就是知心姐姐米娅专栏呀！"米娅回答，"我来帮同学们解决问题。"

"大家需要这样的栏目吗？"艾拉问。

米娅眉毛一挑说："当然！"

"当然不需要！"路易斯说，"同学们都喜欢猜谜语，听笑话。比如：一只半鸡在一天半下了一个半鸡蛋，那……"

"快算了吧！"米娅打断了路易斯的话，"绕口令吗？那还不如这个：土拨鼠拨土拔树！"

　　乔伊一跃而起："土拨鼠！对了，野生动植物专栏怎么样？我今天在足球场上看到小水塘里有一只绿头鸭和……"

　　"那是只呆头鸭！"米娅说道，"我扔给它一片薯片，它反倒钻进树丛里去了。"

　　"也许它在筑巢呢！"乔伊说。

　　米娅瞪了他一眼说："在足球场上？"

　　乔伊泄气地坐下来。

"其实，"我说，"我也很喜欢笑话或野生动植物之类的内容。"

米娅看着我说："我也一样，所以我在写一部《旋风小马》的小说。"

"你是说你的宠物小矮马？它也算野生动物吗？"路易斯反问道。

"那当然！"

天哪，我心想，那可差远了。

米娅戴上了遮阳帽说道："我很忙。我戴上这个的时候，谁都不许讲话！"

屋里一下子安静了。"例会结束了？"路易斯问。米娅指指自己的遮阳帽。

"例会还没结束呢！"艾拉说，"我想写一个体育专栏，有很多采访的那种。"

"已经有人写了。"米娅说，"牛仔女孩米娅专栏！"

艾拉眨眨眼睛："你采访你自己？"

"体育专栏？"路易斯问。

"没错！"米娅说，"我得走了！再见！"

　　我们追着米娅出来。"停下！"艾拉喊道，"我们来看看同学们真正喜欢什么吧！"

　　"我打赌，一定不是米娅长米娅短的内容！"路易斯说。

　　"我们问问大家怎么样？"乔伊说。

　　"好，我们来做一个调查。"我给乔伊竖起了大拇指。

　　"那好，"米娅说，"明天开始吧。我会把你们的调查结果登在报纸上。艾米负责拍照。"

　　听起来挺好玩儿的！

第二天，米娅向我挥舞着一沓信说："读读这些信，看我的建议有多好！"

"你已经开始了？"我说，"那调查呢？要是没有人想看知心姐姐米娅栏目呢？"

"他们一定会的！"米娅说完，把那些信递给了我。

亲爱的米娅：

我的一个朋友是个球霸，怎么才能让她变成一个有团队精神的好队员呢？

一个不合群的人

亲爱的不合群的人：

做个强者，不要抱怨！好好练球，也许她就会把球传给你了。

米娅

亲爱的米娅：

我遇到数学难题的时候，总是害怕，最后就放弃了，我该怎么办？

一个急需帮助的人

亲爱的急需帮助的人：

放弃就等于失败。每个问题都有答案。你最近有没有好好读数学书？

米娅

亲爱的米娅：

我特别特别想养一只羊。可我老妈就是不同意。

一个没有宠物的孩子

亲爱的没有宠物的孩子：

请你把养羊的理由列出来，并用你妈妈的名字给小羊命名。我就是这样得到我的宠物小矮马的。

米娅

13

我看看米娅:"你真的认为这个没有宠物的孩子的妈妈会愿意有只羊跟她自己的名字一样吗?"

"为什么不呢?你不愿意吗?"

"我不愿意,老实说,你的宠物小矮马算不上野生动物。"

米娅一把抢回了信:"怎么不算,就算!"

哼,我心想,咱们走着瞧!

上午课间休息的时候，调查开始了。

"你愿意在我们的校报上看到体育专栏吗？"艾拉问谭雅，"比如有关骑矮种马之类的？"

"不愿意，我喜欢看足球方面的。"她回答道。

"你愿意有个知心姐姐的栏目吗？"路易斯问。

"不，不想看。"

"咔嚓！"我给谭雅照了一张相。

　　"山姆,你愿意在我们的校报上读到关于野生动植物的话题,对不对?"路易斯问,"比如矮种马之类的?"

　　"矮种马? 别开玩笑了!"山姆回答,"要是绿头鸭的话,我喜欢!"

　　"那你愿意看知心姐姐米娅的专栏吗?"

　　山姆做了个鬼脸:"我为什么要听米娅的建议呢?"

　　我给山姆也抓拍了一张。

"嘿，莉莉，"艾拉问，"你会读米娅写的专栏吗？专栏里她会告诉你什么事该怎么做？"

"我更愿意读笑话。"莉莉咯咯笑着说，"我给你们说一个！"

"我们还有急事呢。"艾拉说。

艾拉拉着我离开时，我赶紧给莉莉拍了照片。

"我还没抖包袱呢！"莉莉在我们身后喊道。

"米娅，你看到了吧？"课间过后，路易斯对米娅说，"同学们都喜欢笑话、体育和野生动植物的话题，而不是什么知心姐姐的专栏。"

米娅翻着白眼说："你只不过采访了 3 个同学！这说明不了什么。"

不得不承认，米娅说得有道理。

"如果你想要做调查，要采访 100 个孩子才行！"米娅对我们说，"然后做一张象形统计图。有问题吗？"

"有。"路易斯问，"什么是象形统计图？"

"你不是不愿意听知心姐姐的建议吗？"米娅说完转身走了。

"问我吧！"我说，"我知道，象形统计图就是一种用图形来显示数据的图表。"

我给他们画了一个例子。

"这样啊，"艾拉说，"我觉得我懂了。"

最喜欢的季节	
春	👤👤👤
夏	👤👤👤👤
秋	👤👤
冬	👤

于是，我们继续调查，调查，再调查。

终于,我们来到艾拉家开始做象形统计图了。

"我的手都画累了。"路易斯嘟囔道。

"我也是。"乔伊说,"我讨厌画这些小人儿!"

"快画完了。"我对他们说。

艾拉叹了口气:"我再去取些纸来。"

第二天早上，我们去找米娅。

"我们总共调查了 100 个同学。"艾拉说完和乔伊打开了我们做好的图表。

"请看！"路易斯说，"40 个同学支持笑话和谜语专栏，30 个支持野生动植物专栏，20 个支持体育专栏，只有 10 个人选知心姐姐专栏！"

说完，路易斯得意地跳起舞来。

我看出来米娅有些不痛快，可是她在尽量掩饰她的不快。"不好意思，各位。"她说，"你们的图表太大了，报纸登不下呀。"

　　"你生气是因为我们的调查结果不是你想要的。"艾拉说。

　　米娅戴上了遮阳帽，向图书馆跑去。

"我不干了。"乔伊说。

"我也不干了！"艾拉说，"我讨厌办报纸。"

"做个强者，不要抱怨！"我对大家说，"咱们能找到办法！"

"别劝我们了。"路易斯说，"我们都退出了！"

好吧，我心想，这回轮到米娅听我的了。

我冲进图书馆。

"把这个东西摘掉！"我大声说。

米娅用两只手捂住遮阳帽。

"你说每个问题都有答案。"我说道，"可为什么你不帮我们想想办法呢？"

"我还忙着呢！"米娅干巴巴地回答。

"你还特别霸道！其他同学都退出了。我也要退出！"

过了一会儿，我在柜子里发现了一张纸条：

亲爱的艾米：

不论干什么事，我总觉得一定得做个领导者，可这样一来，朋友们就不愿意跟我好了。你有什么建议吗？

米娅

另：想把象形统计图做小一点儿吗？试试看，每个小人代表不止一个人。

我回了一张字条：

亲爱的米娅：

我的建议吗？做个领导者吧！不过，也给其他人闪光的机会。

艾米

另：谢谢你的小建议！

我飞奔出图书馆。"嗨，我们的问题解决了！"我把米娅的建议告诉了大家。

"这样可以吗？"乔伊问。

"你们想，"我说，"有 40 个人选笑话和谜语。如果我们一个小人代表 10 张选票的话……"

"那画 4 个小人就可以代表 40 张选票了！"路易斯说，"这样图表就大小合适了！"

每个象形统计图都有一句说明文字，告诉你每个图形符号代表什么意思，这叫图例。

例如，每个 🧍 代表 10 张选票。

第二天，我把完成的象形统计图交给了米娅。

"很好！"她说，"这样就能印了。"

"在首页吗？有笑话和谜语专栏吗？"

"为什么没有？"米娅说，"你们当真想看关于呆头鸭的野生动物文章？不想看会跳花步的小矮马的故事吗？"

"对。不过你可以保留知心姐姐专栏。"我朝米娅挤挤眼说道，"只要别写太长就行！"

"那咱俩合作知心姐姐专栏好不好？"米娅问我，"我们俩搭档。"

　　"权益均等？"

　　"完全均等！"米娅说，"艾米，怎么样？求你求你求你啦！"

　　我捂着耳朵笑着说："好吧，好吧！"

　　大家跑到教室外面,找到另外几个同学。

　　"嘿,乔伊!"米娅说,"给我们照张相!哦,不对!我是说,麻烦你给我们拍一张合影可以吗?"

　　米娅和我张开双臂,和伙伴们站成一排。大家紧紧地靠在一起,在镜头前露出开心的笑容。

　　艾米和米娅,我们两个好朋友,不论遇到什么事,都会有办法!

体育专栏

谭雅的足球梦　　供稿人：吴拉

临门一脚！球进啦！这就是她，我们的足球女将谭雅同学，她是我们学校的超级足球明星，在周五晚上的足球比赛上，她又踢进了决定性的一球。

摄影：艾米

最佳运动

这位教练

任意球

惊人！

被罚的

守门员

虚晃

入网

赢球！

校园小记者

来自你我中间，记录无限快乐！

调查结果新鲜出炉！

本报记者采访了 100 位同学，请他们说出希望在我们的报纸上看到哪些方面的内容。请看这些同学的选择！

你最愿意读到的专栏

体育	👤 👤		
野生动植物	👤 👤 👤		
笑话和谜语	👤 👤 👤 👤		
知心姐姐	👤		

注：每个 👤 代表 10 张选票

笑话和谜语

祝你笑口常开！

一位爸爸问孩子："你知道南非有什么稀有动物吗？"儿子说："有北极熊。"爸爸说："孩子，在非洲是找不到北极熊的。"儿子回答："所以才说它是稀有动物啊……"

供稿人：莉莉

摄影：艾米

路易斯的谜语

一只半鸡在一天半下了一个半鸡蛋，那它总共下了多少鸡蛋呢？

答案：一个鸡蛋

野生动植物

来自绿塘的鸭鸣　供稿人：乔伊

你喜欢绿头鸭吗？我的朋友山姆很喜欢。上周，他在我们的足球场附近发现了一只绿头鸭。

公绿头鸭羽毛艳丽，却是个唱歌跑调儿的大嗓门儿。母绿头鸭的叫声好听多了，可它们的模样很平常。

绿头鸭喜欢水草茂盛的环境，它们吃种子、蚯蚓、浆果、小鱼，甚至土豆片……绿头鸭的一生

欣喜的山姆　摄影：艾米

知心小姐妹

供稿人：艾米和米娅

艾米和米娅　摄影：乔伊

亲爱的艾米和米娅：

我特别特别想养一只羊，可老妈就是不同意。

一个没有宠物的孩子

亲爱的没有宠物的孩子：

问你老妈能不能养只猫。至少猫咪可以让你抱呀！

艾米和米娅

亲爱的艾米和米娅：

我一遇到数学难题就害怕，就想放弃，我该怎么办？

一个急需帮助的人

亲爱的急需帮助的人：

去上一个课外辅导班怎么样？会有效果的！

艾米和米娅

亲爱的艾米和米娅：

我的好友是个球霸，怎么才能让她变成一个有团队精神的好队员呢？

一个不合群的人

亲爱的不合群的人：

给她写一张纸条，告诉她你的感受吧。

另：一定要真诚！一定要实话实说！

艾米和米娅

象形统计图

请看下面的象形统计图。你能得到哪些信息?

最喜欢的影片类型						
卡通	◉	◉	◉	◉	◉	◉
喜剧	◉	◉	◉	◉		
悬疑	◉	◉				
野生动物	◉	◉	◉	◉		

2+2+2+2+2+2=12 票

2+2+2+2=8 票

2+2=4 票

2+2+2+2=8 票

每个 ◉ 代表 2 票

如果代表不同的票数呢?

最喜欢的影片类型			
卡通	◉	◉	◉
喜剧	◉	◉	
悬疑	◉		
野生动物	◉	◉	

4+4+4=12 票

4+4=8 票

4 票

4+4=8 票

每个 ◉ 代表 4 票

为什么需要有一个图标表示 $\frac{1}{2}$?

提示:8 票的一半是 4 票

◉的一半是 ◖

最喜欢的影片类型		
卡通	◉	◖
喜剧	◉	
悬疑	◖	
野生动物	◉	

8+4=12 票

8 票

4 票

8 票

每个 ◉ 代表 8 票

亲爱的家长朋友,请您和孩子一起完成下面这些内容,会有更大的收获哟!

提高阅读能力

- 阅读封面,包括书名、作者、绘者等内容。和孩子聊聊,这本书会是一个什么样的故事? 图中哪个孩子看起来最引人注目?

- 读故事。当米娅对其他同学说,她来写关于她的宠物小马以及体育栏目的时候,其他同学的反应如何? 他们对米娅戴的遮阳帽有什么感觉?

- 请翻到第 13 页,读一读同学们写给米娅的信。你们觉得米娅的建议如何?

- 请翻到第 25 页,读一读米娅写给艾米的信,你们觉得米娅写这样一封信需要很大决心和勇气吗? 为什么? 米娅接受艾米的建议了吗? 你是怎么知道的?

33

巩固数学概念

- 请看第 22~23 页上的象形统计图。这次调查说明了什么现象？同学们希望米娅的校园报应该多刊登什么样的稿件呢？米娅需要四种类型都尝试吗？为什么？
- 请看第 30 页的象形统计图。每个小人儿代表几票？几位同学喜欢体育栏目？几位同学喜欢野生动植物的栏目？
- 请看第 15~17 页，如果把谭雅、山姆和莉莉的选择画成象形统计图，会是什么样的？和 30 页上的象形图标相比有什么不同？
- 在第 30 页上的象形统计图中，一个小人儿表示 10 张选票。假设一个小人儿表示 5 票，那新的象形统计图会是什么样的？结果会不一样吗？为什么？

生活中的数学

请孩子根据以下题目开展一项调查。朋友们最喜欢什么体育项目？最喜欢读什么书？最喜欢什么电子游戏？请把调查结果用象形统计图展示出来吧。

你知道喜欢哪种水果的小朋友最多吗？请你在最受欢迎的水果下面打"√"。

我要用画图的方法把调查结果记录下来！

( ) ( ) ( ) ( )

我们要采访 100 名同学,把他们喜欢的栏目记录下来。

你最愿意读到的栏目

体育	👤 👤
野生动植物	👤 👤 👤
笑话和谜语	👤 👤 👤 👤
知心姐姐	👤

每个 👤 代表 10 张选票。那么,喜欢体育栏目的同学有( )人。

请问:他们一共进了(　　)个球。

37

下面是 4 个小朋友在图书馆借书的情况。

15 本	15 本	9 本	12 本

我知道了！我借的本数可以画 5 个 ●。

如果一个 ● 表示 3 本书,你能在下面的象形统计图中把每个小朋友借书的数量表示出来吗?

比 少借( )本书。

明明、聪聪、小刚 3 个好朋友帮王爷爷种树。

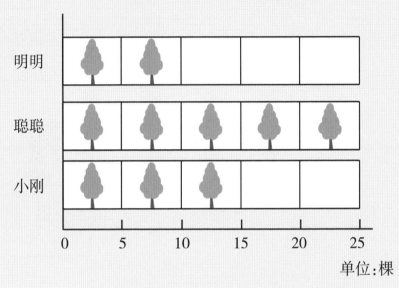

单位:棵

你知道上面的象形统计图中每个 🌲 表示（　　）棵树吗?

小猴子一家到桃园摘桃子，下面是它们摘桃子的数量统计图。

猴爸爸	猴妈妈	猴哥哥	猴弟弟
8个	10个	6个	2个

你还可以用涂格子的方法表示小猴子一家摘桃子的情况。

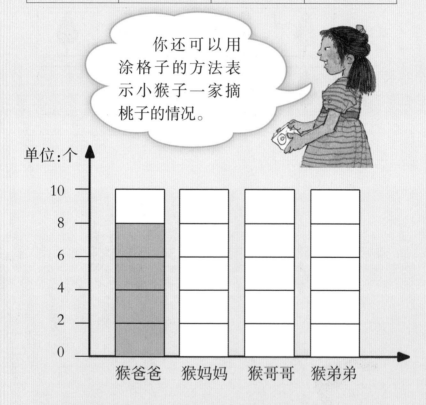

请你用涂格子的方法完成象形统计图，并回答：

①猴妈妈比猴弟弟多摘了(　　)个桃子。

②每个格子代表(　　)个桃子。

互动练习

我调查了我们班喜欢吃蔬菜的情况！

12 人	10 人	11 人	15 人	8 人

根据示例，你知道怎样能表示出喜欢每种蔬菜的同学数量吗？

单位：人

16
14
12
10
8
6
4
2
0

我知道！可以涂半格来表示 1 人！

请你也用涂格子的方法完成，并回答下列问题：

①每个格子代表（　）人。

②喜欢 🍆 和 🍅 的一共有（　）人。

41

互动练习1:

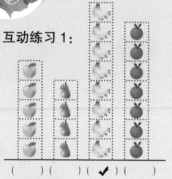

( ) ( ) (✓) ( )

互动练习2:

20

互动练习3:

乔伊 艾拉 路易斯 米娅
( ) ( ) ( ) (✓)

10

互动练习4:

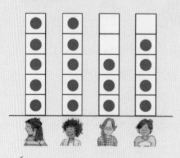

6

互动练习5:

5

互动练习6:

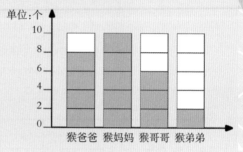

①8 ②2

互动练习7:

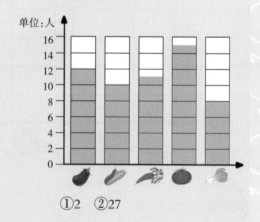

①2 ②27

(习题设计:董惠平 张 芳)

Ask Mia

"I'm going to meet with Mr. Albee about starting a newspaper," Mia said. "You in?"

"Sure!" I told her.

"But Amy," said Mia, "I'll do the talking."

Mia likes to do things her way.

And her way works—most of the time.

Mr. Albee listened while Mia talked. And talked. "A newspaper will help with math, science, and reading. So puh-leeeaze! Can we do it? Please-pleaseplease?"

Mr. Albee smiled. "Okay, okay— I give in!"

"Thanks, Mr. A!" Mia said. She winked at me.

Mia does make things happen!

"So Amy, do you want to be the photographer?" Mia handed me her digital camera. "You can use this."

"Cool!" I said. "Can I also be a reporter?"

"Come to the meeting," said Mia. "We'll talk."

"We'll talk" means no. But oh, so what. It would be fun using Mia's camera.

Ella, Luis, and Joey were at the meeting, too. "What should we put in the paper?" Ella saked.

"Jokes!" Luis said. "Kids can send

them in."

"Mmmm, not sure," said Mia. "I've already asked kids to send in letters to Ask Mia."

"What is that?" said Ella.

"My advice column!" Mia replied. "I'm telling kids how to solve their problems."

"Do kids even want advice?" Ella asked. Mia raised an eyebrow. "Of course."

"Of course not!" said Luis. "Kids want jokes and quizzes. Like, 'If a hen-and-a-half lays an egg-and-a-half in a day-and-a-half, then how many—'"

"T-t-t-t," interrupted Mia. "That's worse than woodchucks chucking wood."

Joey jumped up. "Woodchucks! How about a wildlife column? Today I saw a mallard duck sitting in a puddle on the soccer field, and—"

"That duck is a dope," said Mia. "I threw it a potato chip, and it ran into the bushes."

"Maybe it's building a nest!" said Joey.

Mia stared at him. "On the soccer field?"

Joey slumped back into his chair.

"Actually," I said. "I like jokes. Wildlife, too."

Mia looked at me. "So do I. That's

why I'm writing my Wild About Ponies story."

"Starring your pony—as wildlife?" Luis asked.

"Correct."

Gosh, I thought. That was a stretch.

Mia put on a visor. "I've got a lot to do. When I'm wearing this, no one talks."

The room grew quiet.

"The meeting's over?" asked Luis. Mia pointed to her visor.

"We're not finished," Ella said. "I want to write a sports column—with interviews!"

"It's already done," said Mia. "Mia the Cowgirl."

Ella blinked. "You interviewed yourself?"

"For the sports column?" Luis asked.

"Yup," Mia said. "Gotta go now! Buh-bye!"

We followed Mia outside. "Stop!" Ella called. "Let's find out what kids really want to read!"

"I'll bet it's not Mia and more Mia," Luis said.

"Why don't we ask around?" said Joey.

"Yes—take a survey!" I gave him a thumbs-up.

"Fine," said Mia. "Start tomorrow. I'll put your results in the paper. Amy can take photos."

That sounded like fun!

The next morning, Mia waved a handful of letters at me. "Read these. Wait until you see how good my advice is."

"You already started?" I asked.

"What about the survey? What if no one wants an advice column?"

"Everyone will want it," said Mia. She gave me the letters.

Dear Mia,
Someone I know is a ball hog. How can I make her be a better team player?
Left out

Dear Left out,
Be a winner, not a whiner. Learn to play better. Then maybe she'll pass you the ball.
Mia

Dear Mia,
When I can't figure out math problems I freak out and give up. I just don't get it.
Help!

Dear Help,
Quitters are losers. There's a solution to every problem. Have you read your math book lately?
Mia

Dear Mia,
I really want a goat but my mom says no.
Petless

Dear Petless,
Make a chart showing reasons for having a goat, and name the goat after your mother.
That's how I got my pony.
Mia

I looked at Mia. "You really think Petless's mom would want a goat named after her?"

"Why not? Wouldn't you?"

"No. And to be honest, your pony doesn't belong in Wildlife."

Mia grabbed the letters back. "Yes, it does!"

Hmm, I thought. We'll see about that.

The survey began at morning recess.

"Would you like a sports column in our newspaper?" Ella asked Tanya. "Featuring pony riding, maybe?"

"No. Featuring soccer," she said.

"Do you like advice columns?" asked Luis.

"No, I don't."

Click! I took Tanya's picture.

"Sam, you like to read about wildlife, right?" Luis asked. "Like ponies, for example?"

"Ponies, no," replied Sam. "Mallards, yes."

"Would you read an advice column written by Mia?" Ella asked.

Sam made a face. "Why would I need advice from Mia?"

I snapped his picture.

"Hey, Lily?" Ella asked. "Think you'd read a column where Mia tells you what to do?"

"I'd rather read jokes." Lily started to giggle. "Listen to this one!"

"We're kind of in a hurry here," said Ella.

I took her picture as Ella pulled me away.

"But what about the punch line?" Lily called.

"See, Mia?" Luis said after recess. "Kids like jokes and sports and wildlife—not advice."

Mia rolled her eyes. "You only interviewed three kids! That doesn't prove anything."

I had to admit, she was right.

"If you want to do a survey, talk to a hundred kids!" Mia told us. "Then make a pictograph. Any questions?"

"Yeah," said Luis. "What's a pictograph?"

"Don't ask Mia," Mia said, and walked off.

"Ask me!" I said.

"I know. Well, sort of. A pictograph is a graph with pictures."

I drew one for them.

"Ah!" said Ella. "I get it—I think."

So we surveyed.

And surveyed. And surveyed.

Later we went to Ella's house to make our pictograph. "My hand is so tired," grumbled Luis.

"Mine, too," said Joey. "I'm sick, sick, sick of stick people!"

"We're almost done," I told them.

Ella sighed. "I'll get more paper."

The next morning we marched up to Mia.

"We surveyed a hundred kids," Ella began. She and Joey unrolled the graph.

"Tada!" said Luis. "Forty for jokes and quizzes, thirty for wildlife, twenty for sports, and only ten for advice!"

He did a victory dance.

I could tell Mia was miffed, but she was trying not to show it. "Sorry, guys," she said. "This is way too big to fit in the paper."

"You're just mad because you don't like the way the survey came out," said Ella.

On went the visor. Mia scuttled back into the library.

"I give up," Joey said.

"Me, too," said Ella. "I hate the newspaper."

"Let's be winners, not whiners!" I told them. "We can figure this out!"

"Leave us alone," said Luis. "We all quit."

Okay, I thought. It was time for Mia to listen to me for a change.

I stormed inside.

"Take that off," I demanded.

Mia held onto her visor with both hands.

"You say every problem has a solution," I said. "Why don't you help us find one?"

"I'm busy," Mia told me crisply.

"And bossy! The other kids are quitting. And so am I."

Later I found a note in my cubby.

Dear Amy,
I feel like I always have to be the star. It ruins my friendships. Any advice?
Mia
P.S. Want to make a pictograph smaller? Let each stick figure stand for more than one vote.

I wrote back.

Dear Mia,
My advice? Be a star—but let others shine, too.
Amy
P.S. Thanks for the pictograph tip.

I hurried outside. "Hey, guys! Our problem is solved." I told every-one about Mia's tip.

"How does that help us?" asked Joey.

"Think about it," I said. "Jokes and quizzes got forty votes. So if we make one stick person stand for ten votes…"

"Then four stick people will stand for forty votes," Luis said. "And the pictograph will fit!"

The next day, I gave Mia our new pictograph. "Mm hm," she said. "I can print this."

"On the front page? With jokes and quizzes?"

"Oh, why not?" said Mia. "But you really want a wildlife story about a dizzy duck? Instead of a prancing pony?"

"Yup. You can still do an advice column, though." I winked at her. "If you keep it short."

"Why don't the two of us share the advice column?" Mia asked. "We can be partners."

"Equal partners?"

"Totally," said Mia. "So, how about it, Amy? Pleasepleaseplease?"

I covered my ears and laughed. "Okay, okay!"

We ran outside to find the other kids.

"Hey, Joey!" called Mia. "Take our picture! Oops, I mean—will you please take our picture?"

Mia and I slung our arms around each other's shoulders and smiled for the camera.

Amy and Mia, we were ready to make things happen!